SILLY SENTENCES
HANDWRITING WORKBOOK

MODERN KID PRESS

D1472139

Want free goodies?!

Email us at

modernkidpress@gmail.com

Title the email "Silly Sentences!"
and we'll send some goodies
your way!

Questions & Customer Service:
Email us at modernkidpress@gmail.com!

This book belongs to:

_____

. . . .

_____

Trace the letter in your best handwriting.

A A A A A A A A A A A A A A A A

a a a a a a a a a a a a a a a a a

First trace the sentence. Then write it on your own.

Astronauts do aerials over asteroids.

Astronauts do aerials over asteroids.

Acrobats feed ants apricots in Australia.

Acrobats feed ants apricots in Australia.

Write your own silly sentence below. Then draw the absolute silliest picture to go with it!

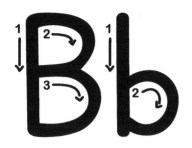  

Trace the letter in your best handwriting.

B B B B B B B B B B B B B

b b b b b b b b b b b b b b

First trace the sentence. Then write it on your own.

Buffalo walk backwards on their birthday.

Buffalo walk backwards on their birthday.

Bears who eat their boogers are bad.

Bears who eat their boogers are bad.

Write your own silly sentence below. Then draw the absolute silliest picture to go with it!

Trace the letter in your best handwriting.

C C C C C C C C C C C C C C

c c c c c c c c c c c c c c c c c c

First trace the sentence. Then write it on your own.

Candy canes cause craziness.

Candy canes cause craziness.

The clever crab cuddled the cake.

The clever crab cuddled the cake.

Write your own silly sentence below. Then draw the absolute silliest picture to go with it!

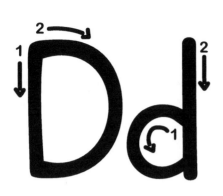

Trace the letter in your best handwriting.

D D D D D D D D D D D D D D D D

d d d d d d d d d d d d d d d d d

First trace the sentence. Then write it on your own.

Daring dogs dance during dodgeball.

Daring dogs dance during dodgeball.

Dinosaurs devour donuts daily, dude.

Dinosaurs devour donuts daily, dude.

Write your own silly sentence below. Then draw the absolute silliest picture to go with it!

Trace the letter in your best handwriting.

First trace the sentence. Then write it on your own.

Elephants eat everything in Egypt.

Elephants eat everything in Egypt.

Eels do the electric slide on the escalator.

Eels do the electric slide on the escalator.

Write your own silly sentence below. Then draw the absolute silliest picture to go with it!

Ff

Trace the letter in your best handwriting.

F F F F F F F F F F F F F F F F

f f f f f f f f f f f f f f f f f f f f f f f f f f f

First trace the sentence. Then write it on your own.

Flamingoes play freeze tag on Fridays.

Flamingoes play freeze tag on Fridays.

Fairies fly faster than dragon flames flash.

Fairies fly faster than dragon flames flash.

Write your own silly sentence below. Then draw the absolute silliest picture to go with it!

Trace the letter in your best handwriting.

G G G G G G G G G G G G G G G

g g g g g g g g g g g g g g g g

First trace the sentence. Then write it on your own.

Goodness gracious, get off that gorilla!

Goodness gracious, get off that gorilla!

Don't chew grape gum while ghost hunting.

Don't chew grape gum while ghost hunting.

Write your own silly sentence below. Then draw the absolute silliest picture to go with it!

_____

_____

_____

_____

_____

_____

Trace the letter in your best handwriting.

H H H H H H H H H H H H H H H

h h h h h h h h h h h h h h h

First trace the sentence. Then write it on your own.

Hippos wear high tops on the high dive.

Hippos wear high tops on the high dive.

Hedgehogs hula hoop during hide and seek.

Hedgehogs hula hoop during hide and seek.

Write your own silly sentence below. Then draw the absolute silliest picture to go with it!

Trace the letter in your best handwriting.

I I I I I I I I I I I I I I I I I

i i i i i i i i i i i i i i i i i i i i i i i i i i i i

First trace the sentence. Then write it on your own.

I live in an igloo on an island in Indiana.

I live in an igloo on an island in Indiana.

Ice cream is an ingenious invention!

Ice cream is an ingenious invention!

Write your own silly sentence below. Then draw the absolute silliest picture to go with it!

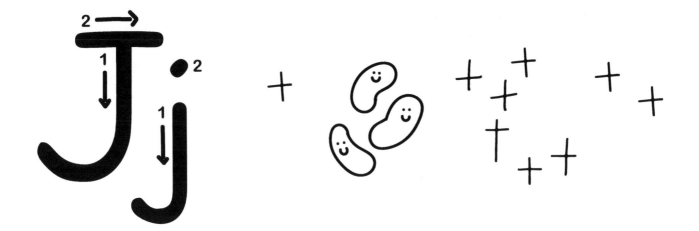

Trace the letter in your best handwriting.

J J J J J J J J J J J J J

j j j j j j j j j j j j j j j j j j j j j j j j j

First trace the sentence. Then write it on your own.

Jaguars wear jeans while jogging.

Jaguars wear jeans while jogging.

Jelly beans do jumping jacks in jail.

Jelly beans do jumping jacks in jail.

Write your own silly sentence below. Then draw the absolute silliest picture to go with it!

Trace the letter in your best handwriting.

K K K K K K K K K K K K K

k k k k k k k k k k k k k k

First trace the sentence. Then write it on your own.

Koalas sing karaoke to kangaroos.

Koalas sing karaoke to kangaroos.

Kittens play the kazoo during kickball.

Kittens play the kazoo during kickball.

Write your own silly sentence below. Then draw the absolute silliest picture to go with it!

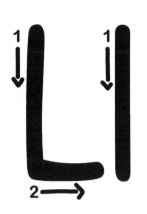  

Trace the letter in your best handwriting.

L L L L L L L L L L L L L L L L L

l l l l l l l l l l l l l l l l l l l l l l l l l l l l l

First trace the sentence. Then write it on your own.

Librarians laugh loudly in London.

Librarians laugh loudly in London.

Llamas love licking licorice for lunch.

Llamas love licking licorice for lunch.

Write your own silly sentence below. Then draw the absolute silliest picture to go with it!

Trace the letter in your best handwriting.

M M M M M M M M M M

m m m m m m m m m m m

First trace the sentence. Then write it on your own.

Mermaids like to munch on mini macarons.

Mermaids like to munch on mini macarons.

Magicians make magical macaroni!

Magicians make magical macaroni!

Write your own silly sentence below. Then draw the absolute silliest picture to go with it!

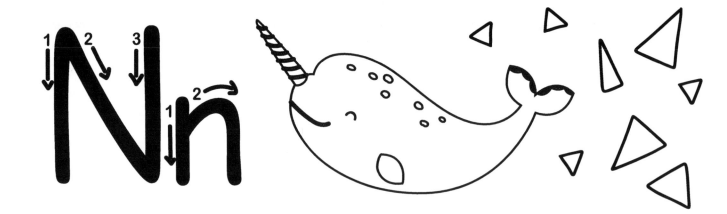

Trace the letter in your best handwriting.

N N N N N N N N N N N N N N

n n n n n n n n n n n n n n n n

First trace the sentence. Then write it on your own.

Narwhals never nap at night.

Narwhals never nap at night.

Ninjas only need nunchucks to ninJAM!

Ninjas only need nunchucks to ninJAM!

Write your own silly sentence below. Then draw the absolute silliest picture to go with it!

Trace the letter in your best handwriting.

O O O O O O O O O O O O

o o o o o o o o o o o o o o o o o o o

First trace the sentence. Then write it on your own.

An otter orders hourderves.

An otter orders hourderves.

Orange you glad oreos are in outer space?

Orange you glad oreos are in outer space?

Write your own silly sentence below. Then draw the absolute silliest picture to go with it!

Trace the letter in your best handwriting.

P P P P P P P P P P P P P P P

p p p p p p p p p p p p p p p

First trace the sentence. Then write it on your own.

Pirates pick their nose in parades.

Pirates pick their nose in parades.

Penguins parachute out of paper airplanes.

Penguins parachute out of paper airplanes.

Write your own silly sentence below. Then draw the absolute silliest picture to go with it!

Trace the letter in your best handwriting.

Q Q Q Q Q Q Q Q Q Q Q Q Q

q q q q q q q q q q q q q q q q q q q q q q q q q

First trace the sentence. Then write it on your own.

Queens quack during the quiet game.

Queens quack during the quiet game.

Quirky quails quickly eat quesadillas.

Quirky quails quickly eat quesadillas.

Write your own silly sentence below. Then draw the absolute silliest picture to go with it!

Trace the letter in your best handwriting.

R R R R R R R R R R R R R R

r r r r r r r r r r r r r r r r r r r r r r r r r

First trace the sentence. Then write it on your own.

Rockstars rollerskate over rainbows.

Rockstars rollerskate over rainbows.

Robots rock to the radio in a rocket ship!

Robots rock to the radio in a rocket ship!

Write your own silly sentence below. Then draw the absolute silliest picture to go with it!

S s

Trace the letter in your best handwriting.

S S S S S S S S S S S S S S

s s s s s s s s s s s s s s s s

First trace the sentence. Then write it on your own.

Spies use special slime to spook villains.

Spies use special slime to spook villains.

Super heros slip 'n slide in the summer.

Super heros slip 'n slide in the summer.

Write your own silly sentence below. Then draw the absolute silliest picture to go with it!

Trace the letter in your best handwriting.

T T T T T T T T T T T T T T T T T

t t t t t t t t t t t t t t t t t t t t t t t t t t t

First trace the sentence. Then write it on your own.

Tiny tigers play tag on tiny trampolines.

Tiny tigers play tag on tiny trampolines.

Teachers take their tricycles to test toys.

Teachers take their tricycles to test toys.

Write your own silly sentence below. Then draw the absolute silliest picture to go with it!

Trace the letter in your best handwriting.

U U U U U U U U U U U U U U

u u u u u u u u u u u u u u u u u u

First trace the sentence. Then write it on your own.

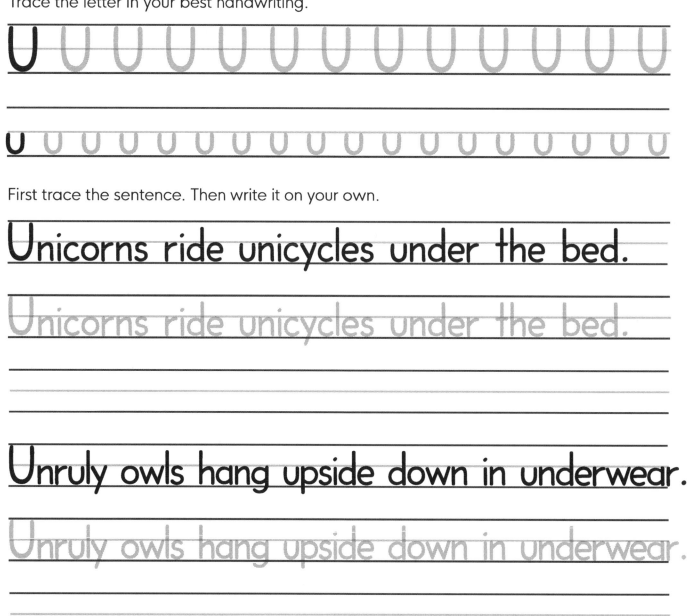

Unicorns ride unicycles under the bed.

Unicorns ride unicycles under the bed.

Unruly owls hang upside down in underwear.

Unruly owls hang upside down in underwear.

Write your own silly sentence below. Then draw the absolute silliest picture to go with it!

Trace the letter in your best handwriting.

V V V V V V V V V V V V V V V V

v v v v v v v v v v v v v v v v v v v

First trace the sentence. Then write it on your own.

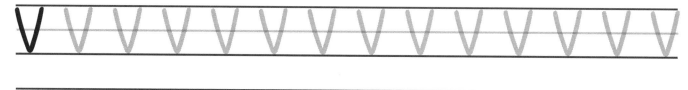

Villains park their vans in volcanoes.

Villains park their vans in volcanoes.

Violet makes videos of veggies playing violins.

Violet makes videos of veggies playing violins.

Write your own silly sentence below. Then draw the absolute silliest picture to go with it!

Trace the letter in your best handwriting.

W W W W W W W W W W W

w w w w w w w w w w w w

First trace the sentence. Then write it on your own.

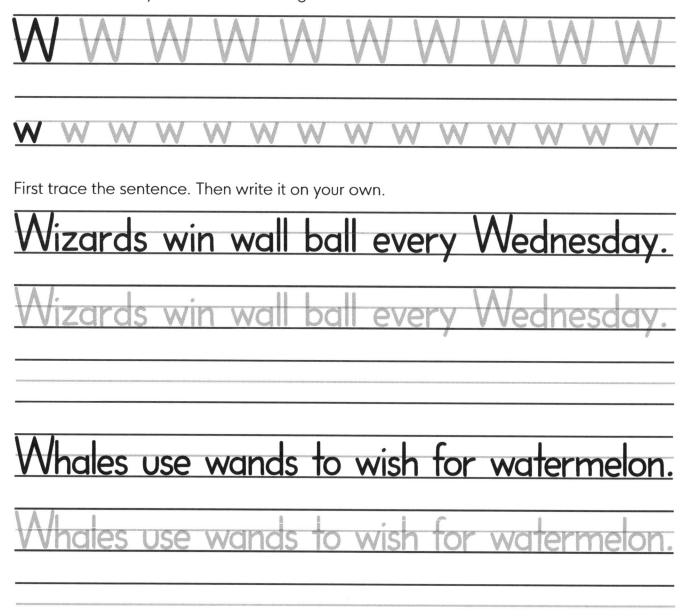

Wizards win wall ball every Wednesday.

Wizards win wall ball every Wednesday.

Whales use wands to wish for watermelon.

Whales use wands to wish for watermelon.

Write your own silly sentence below. Then draw the absolute silliest picture to go with it!

Trace the letter in your best handwriting.

First trace the sentence. Then write it on your own.

The fox took extra care of his x-ray fish.

The fox took extra care of his x-ray fish.

Six oxen played xylophones in the park.

Six oxen played xylophones in the park.

Write your own silly sentence below. Then draw the absolute silliest picture to go with it!

Trace the letter in your best handwriting.

Y Y Y Y Y Y Y Y Y Y Y Y Y Y Y Y

y y y y y y y y y y y y y y y y y

First trace the sentence. Then write it on your own.

Yaks do yoga while eating yummy yams.

Yaks do yoga while eating yummy yams.

You can't yawn while you yo-yo, you know.

You can't yawn while you yo-yo, you know.

Write your own silly sentence below. Then draw the absolute silliest picture to go with it!

Trace the letter in your best handwriting.

Z Z Z Z Z Z Z Z Z Z Z Z Z Z

z z z z z z z z z z z z z z z z

First trace the sentence. Then write it on your own.

Zombies ride zebras through the zoo.

Zombies ride zebras through the zoo.

Zig Zag man zoomed zero miles per hour.

Zig Zag man zoomed zero miles per hour.

Write your own silly sentence below. Then draw the absolute silliest picture to go with it!

Decode Mode!

Use the code below to write the letters above the numbered spaces and decode the silly sentence!

A	B	C	D	E	F	G	H	I	J	K	L	M
1	2	3	4	5	6	7	8	9	10	11	12	13

N	O	P	Q	R	S	T	U	V	W	X	Y	Z
14	15	16	17	18	19	20	21	22	23	24	25	26

7 15 1 20 19   7 15   6 15 18   7 15 12 4

15 14   7 18 5 5 14   7 15   3 1 18 20 19 !

. . . .

12 5 16 18 5 3 8 1 21 14 19   12 9 3 11   20 8 5 9 18

12 9 16 19   6 15 18   12 15 12 12 9 16 15 16 19 !

Unscramble This!

Unscramble the letters below to discover the silly sentence!
Hint: This silly sentence focuses on the letter "B"!

Ityt   _____

btiyt   _____

ebelte   _____

ugbs   _____

kieb   _____

ni   __

het   _____

nrba   _____

Now rewrite the sentence below!

____ ____ _____ _____

_____ __ _____ _____ !

Word Search Silliness!

Find the words in the word search below, then put them in the right order to form the silly sentence!

```
A Y C P M T L O R H G P E N C I
L H A L H O B U Y F L R D B J P
P A T A R N E H T D S T A G H L
M R E R J C T R P E A S X T Q A
J W G U P A L A C E N O C R A Y
H E O I Q J D S C T P I V F D H
Y B R S R P I B F I N E B C V N
V U I H T E C A M E L S N E G Q
F P E V G Y B L J N C Y H S Y A
R L S Z B E H N L A R B T Z N X
X M Q S N A F G K C R Y S T A L
```

CAMELS
PLAY
CATEGORIES
IN

THE
CRYSTAL
PALACE

___ ___ ___ ___

___ ___ ___ !

Decode Mode!

Use the code below to write the letters above the numbered
spaces and decode the silly sentence!

A	B	C	D	E	F	G	H	I	J	K	L	M
1	2	3	4	5	6	7	8	9	10	11	12	13

N	O	P	Q	R	S	T	U	V	W	X	Y	Z
14	15	16	17	18	19	20	21	22	23	24	25	26

___ ___ ___ ___ ___ ___ ___   ___ ___ ___ ___ ___   ___ ___ ___
19 1   9 12 15 18 19   19 8 15 15 20   6 15 18

___ ___ ___   ___ ___ ___ ___ ___   ___ ___   ___ ___ ___ ___ ___ !
20 8   5   19 20 1 18 19   9 14   19 15 3 11 19

. . . .

___ ___ ___ ___ ___ ___   ___ ___ ___   ___ ___ ___ ___ ___ ___ ___
9   7 14 15 18   5   20 8   5   9 14 19   5   3 20 19

___ ___ ___ ___ ___ ___ ___   ___ ___ ___   ___ ___ ___ ___ ___ ___ !
16 12 1 25   9 14   7   9   3   5   8 15   3 11   5 25

Unscramble This!

Unscramble the letters below to discover the silly sentence!
Hint: This silly sentence focuses on the letter "N"!

eNvre   _____

upt   ____

ondoesl   _____

ni   __

uoyr   ____

sntrolis   _____

ta   __

higtn   _____

Now rewrite the sentence below!

_____ ____ __ _____

_____ __ _____ !

Word Search Silliness!

Find the words in the word search below, then write the silly sentence below using that amazing handwriting!

```
S G N P M T L C R H Q P I B A E
L H A L H O B J Y F L R D A U B
T A T A R N U H T D S T A K H L
A R L R J C R Q P E A S X I R A
J W G U P A G E R H N N Y N A W
H E C I Q J L D C T P I C G S H
F B R E A K A V F V N E B E B I
V R I H T E R G M E L S N S A L
F E Y V G Y S Y J N C Y H Z L E
R A S Z B E H N L A R B T R N X
X D Q S N A F A K Y R C S U G P
```

BURGLARS   WHILE
BREAK   BAKING
DANCE   BREAD

_____ _____ _____

_____ _____ _____ !

Decode Mode!

Use the code below to write the letters above the numbered spaces and decode the silly sentence!

A	B	C	D	E	F	G	H	I	J	K	L	M
1	2	3	4	5	6	7	8	9	10	11	12	13

N	O	P	Q	R	S	T	U	V	W	X	Y	Z
14	15	16	17	18	19	20	21	22	23	24	25	26

___ ___ ___ ___   ___ ___ ___ ___ ___ ___ ___   ___ ___
3 1 20 19   3 1 18 16 15 15 12   20 15

___ ___ ___ ___ ___   ___   ___ ___ ___ ___ !
3 1 20 3 8   1   3 15 12 4

. . . .

___ ___ ___ ___ ___ ___ ___   ___ ___ ___   ___ ___ ___ ___ ___ ,
20 21 18 20 12 5 19   20 1 16   4 1 14 3 5

___ ___ ___ ___ ___ ,   ___ ___ ___   ___ ___ ___ ___ ___ !
20 23 9 18 12   1 14 4   20 1 14 7 15

Word Search Silliness!

Find the words in the word search below, then write the silly
sentence below using that amazing handwriting!

```
H B G J M L T C R S E P I B A Q
F V A L H O B J Y L B R D A U L
C D T A R O U H T N L T A K H S
E R L R J R R Q P R A S M R I A
O I G U P D G E R J W N S P N N
T N C I Q J L D C A H I E G S P
V K R D R A G O N F I E L E B N
E R I H T E R G M V L S S S A L
N E Y V G Y S Y J T E Y H Z L C
B A S Z B E H N L R X B T R N R
Y D I S T R E S S N P C S U G O
```

DAMSELS   DRINK
IN   DRAGON
DISTRESS   DROOL

_____ __ _____

_____ _____ _____ !

Unscramble This!

Unscramble the letters below to discover the silly sentence!
Hint: This silly sentence focuses on the letter "S"!

Ssolth _____

iks ___

deiwsays _____

wond _____

lpispyre _____

ploses _____

Now rewrite the sentence below!

_____ ____ _____

_____ _____ _____ !

Decode Mode!

Use the code below to write the letters above the numbered spaces and decode the silly sentence!

A	B	C	D	E	F	G	H	I	J	K	L	M
1	2	3	4	5	6	7	8	9	10	11	12	13

N	O	P	Q	R	S	T	U	V	W	X	Y	Z
14	15	16	17	18	19	20	21	22	23	24	25	26

___ ___ ___ ___   ___ ___   ___ ___ ___ ___ ___ ___ ___   ___ ___ ___ ___
26   5 21 19   9   19   16 21 26 26 12   5   4   15 22   5 18

___ ___ ___ ___ ___ ___ ___   ___ ___ ___ ___ ___ ___ ___ !
26   9 16 16   9 14   7   26   9 16 16   5 18 19

. . . .

___ ___ ___ ___ ___ ___   ___ ___ ___ ___ ___ ___   ___ ___ ___ ___
1 12   9   5 14 19   1   4 13   9 18   5   1 16   5 19

___ ___ ___ ___ ___ ___ ___ ___ ___   ___ ___ ___ ___ ___ ___ !
1 20 20   1   3 11   9 14   7   1 16 16 12   5 19

Word Search Silliness!

Find the words in the word search below, then write the silly sentence below using that amazing handwriting!

```
A C K H P L T C Q S O P R B A G
F E S L H X F R E N C H D A U L
L G C O K O G H Y N R T Y K H Y
A U P W J V R Q P R A S E R I F
M P J E H D U E U J W N S P N R
I V B T Q N L D C A P I U G S I
N Q R U G S B R H F I E L E B E
G M L O E P R G M R J N G S A S
Z T Y X D T E Y J Y E Y H Z L J
B R O Z B E H J P R X B T H E G
T F B S A R N F S N Q C S U R O
```

FOXES   IN
FRY   THE
FRENCH   FLAMING
FRIES   FIRE

____ __ ____ ____

__ __ _____ ____!

Unscramble This!

Unscramble the letters below to discover the silly sentence!
Hint: This silly sentence focuses on the letter "R"!

aRbtibs _____

irde _____

dar _____

caer _____

arsc _____

ni ___

eht _____

airn _____

Now rewrite the sentence below!

_____ _____ _____ _____

_____ _____ _____ _____

Using your new super power handwriting skills, write a story about aliens invading the earth...

Using your new super power handwriting skills, write a story about humans discovering mermaids...

Using your new super power handwriting skills, write a story about a dog that tells silly jokes...

Using your new super power handwriting skills, write a story about your favorite person...

Using your new super power handwriting skills, write a story about a crazy adventure in the...

Using your new super power handwriting skills, write a story about living in a volcano...

Using your new super power handwriting skills, write a story about traveling to a secret world...

Using your new super power handwriting skills, write a story about you and your best buddy...

Using your new super power handwriting skills, write a story about riding on top of rain clouds...

Using your new super power handwriting skills, write a story about what super power you have...

Using your new super power handwriting skills, write a story about baking a 100 tier cake...

Using your new super power handwriting skills, write a story about bats, cats, and rats...

12686310R00044